THE KEYS TO A

BLESSED

LIFE

The Keys to a Blessed Life Study Guide
Edition 2.0
Copyright © 2015 Rick Warren

PASTORRICK.COM

Published by Purpose Driven Publishers
23182 Arroyo Vista
Rancho Santa Margarita, CA 92688

ISBN: 978-1-4228-0334-9

TABLE OF CONTENTS

UNDERSTANDING YOUR STUDY GUIDE

Here is a brief explanation of the features of this study guide.

CHECKING IN: You will open each meeting with an opportunity for everyone to check in with each other about how you are doing with the weekly assignments. Accountability is a key to success in this study!

KEY VERSE: Each week you will find a key verse or Scripture passage for your group to read together. If someone in the group has a different translation, ask them to read it aloud so the group can get a bigger picture of the meaning of the passage.

VIDEO LESSON: There is a video lesson for the group to watch together each week. Fill in the blanks in the lesson outlines as you watch the video, and be sure to refer back to these outlines during your discussion time.

DISCOVERY QUESTIONS: Each video segment is complemented by several questions for group discussion. Please don't feel pressured to discuss every single question. There is no reason to rush through the answers. Give everyone ample opportunity to share their thoughts. If you don't get through all of the discussion questions, that's okay.

PUTTING IT INTO PRACTICE: This is where the rubber meets the road. We don't want to be just hearers of the Word. We also need to be doers of the Word (James 1:22). These assignments are application exercises that will help you put into practice the truths you have discussed in the lesson.

PRAYER DIRECTION: At the end of each session you will find suggestions for your group prayer time. Praying together is one of the greatest privileges of small group life. Please don't take it for granted.

A Tip for the Host

The study guide material is meant to be your servant, not your master. The point is not to race through the sessions; the point is to take time to let God work in your lives. Nor is it necessary to "go around the circle" before you move on to the next question. Give people the freedom to speak, but don't insist on it. Your group will enjoy deeper, more open sharing and discussion if people don't feel pressured to speak up.

HOW TO USE THIS VIDEO CURRICULUM

Follow these simple steps for a successful small group meeting:

- Open your group meeting by using the **Checking In** section of your study guide.

- Watch the video lesson together and follow along in the outlines in this study guide. Each video lesson is about fifteen minutes long.

- Complete the rest of the discussion materials for each session. Be sure to review the **Putting It Into Practice** section and commit to fulfilling any action steps before your next session.

- Close your time together by following the **Prayer Direction** suggestions.

IT DEPENDS ON WHO YOU DEPEND ON

CHECKING IN

If this is your first time to meet as a group, or if you have any new group members, be sure to introduce yourselves.

This series is about the Beatitudes from the Sermon on the Mount. Take a minute to share what you know about this section of the New Testament and what questions you have about these verses that you hope will be answered in this series.

Make sure to discuss **Group Guidelines** on page 58 to lay the foundation for a healthy group experience.

KEY VERSE

"Blessed are the poor in spirit, for theirs is the kingdom of heaven."
Matthew 5:3 (NIV)

"God blesses those who . . . realize their need for him."
(New Living Translation)

"Who recognize they are spiritually helpless."
(God's Word Translation)

"Who depend only on him."
(Contemporary English Version)

"Who know they have great spiritual needs."
(New Century Version)

*"The Lord God . . . blesses everyone who trusts
him and depends on him."*
Psalm 146:5 (CEV)

• •

TO BE "POOR IN SPIRIT" MEANS

_____.

• •

5 WAYS TO EXPRESS MY DEPENDENCE ON GOD

1. _____

*"There is a way that seems right to a man, but in the end
it leads to death."*
Proverbs 14:12 (NIV)

*"Trust in the Lord with all your heart; do not depend on your own
understanding. Seek his will in all you do, and he will direct your paths.
Don't be impressed with your own wisdom. Instead, respect the Lord and
turn your back on evil."*
Proverbs 3:5-7 (NLT)

• •

How do you get God's wisdom?

- Pray

- Read

"If any of you lack wisdom, you should pray and ask God, who gives it generously and graciously to all."
James 1:5

2. _____

"You bless all who depend on you for their strength."
Psalm 84:5 (CEV)

"Those who trust in the Lord for help will find their strength renewed. They will rise on wings like eagles; they will run and not get weary; they will walk and not grow weak."
Isaiah 40:31 (GNT)

3. _____

While you're waiting, God is working.

• •

"I trust in you, O Lord; I say, 'You are my God. My times are in your hand.'"
Psalm 31:14-15 (ESV)

"[God] has set the right time for everything."
Ecclesiastes 3:11 (GNT)

"I am the Lord, and when it is time, I will make these things happen quickly."
Isaiah 60:22 (NCV)

• •

A delay is not a denial.

4. _____

"God blesses and protects everyone who runs to him."
Psalm 2:12 (CEV)

"I depend on God alone; I put my hope in him. He alone protects and saves me; he is my defender, and I shall never be defeated. My salvation and honor depend on God; he is my strong protector; he is my shelter!"
Psalm 62:5-7 (GNT)

5. _____

"And my God will supply all my needs from his abundant wealth because of what Christ Jesus has done for us."
Philippians 4:19

• •

Your job is a channel, but God is your source.

DISCOVERY QUESTIONS

1. One of the ways to express your dependence on God is to depend on God's wisdom, which can come from both praying and reading the Bible. Which of these is the most challenging for you? Why?

2. Pastor Tom shared the phrase, "While you're waiting, God is working." Looking back on your life, has there been a time of waiting that was frustrating in the moment, but now you see that God was working the whole time?

PUTTING IT INTO PRACTICE

Rate yourself on the "5 Ways to Express
My Dependence on God."

Give yourself a "+" (I'm trusting God pretty well in this area) or a "—" (I need to work on this one this week).

- Depending on God's wisdom _____

- Depending on God's strength _____

- Depending on God's timing _____

- Depending on God's defense _____

- Depending on God's wealth _____

Focus on one area where you need to become more dependent on God. What are some steps you can take that will require you to trust God more?

PRAYER DIRECTION

As you pray together in your small group, ask God to help you depend more on him. Expect God to answer your prayers, and be prepared to take a step of faith.

Now pray for guidance for how to give up control in the areas where you are living independent of God. Tell God you want to trust him and become dependent upon him.

HOW GOD BLESSES BROKEN HEARTS

CHECKING IN

Last week we talked about depending more on God instead of ourselves. Share how you depended on God this week, and describe any obstacles you faced throughout the process.

KEY VERSE

"God blesses those who mourn, for they will be comforted."
Matthew 5:4 (NLT)

GOD DOESN'T EXPECT ME TO BE _____

"There is a time for everything, and a season for every activity under the heavens . . . . a time to weep and a time to laugh, a time to mourn and a time to dance."
Ecclesiastes 3:1, 4 (NIV)

• •

Repression is when I **unconsciously** try to block a painful thought from my mind.

Suppression is when I **consciously** try to block a painful thought from my mind.

∙∙

If I don't let it out, I'll act it out.

"When I kept things to myself, I felt weak deep inside me. I moaned all day long."
Psalm 32:3 (NCV)

"I was mute and silent; I held my peace to no avail, and my distress grew worse."
Psalm 39:2 (ESV)

∙∙

HOW DOES GOD BLESS BROKEN HEARTS?

1. _____

"The Lord is close to the brokenhearted, and he saves those whose spirits have been crushed."
Psalm 34:18 (NCV)

"I will never leave you; I will never abandon you."
Hebrews 13:5 (NCV)

"Our hearts ache, but at the same time we have the joy of the Lord."
2 Corinthians 6:10 (TLB)

2. _____

"[Jesus was] a man of sorrows, acquainted with bitterest grief."
Isaiah 53:3 (TLB)

"When Jesus saw Lazarus' sister sobbing, and saw how all those with her were crying also, his heart was touched, and he was deeply moved . . . Then Jesus started crying. 'See how much he loved Lazarus!' they said."
John 11:33, 36

"He has sent me to comfort all who mourn, to give to those who mourn in Zion joy and gladness instead of grief, a song of praise instead of sorrow."
Isaiah 61:2-3 (GNT)

3. _____

"In Christ we, though many, form one body, and each member belongs to all the others . . . Be devoted to each other like a loving family . . . Rejoice with those who rejoice; mourn with those who mourn."
Romans 12:5, 10, 15 (NIV/GW/NIV)

"Comfort each other and give each other strength."
1 Thessalonians 5:11 (ICB)

• •

- Never minimize another's pain.

- Never rush people.

4. _____

- God uses pain to get your attention.

"God whispers to us in our pleasure, but he shouts
to us in our pain." —C.S. Lewis

"Sometimes it takes a painful experience to make us change our ways."
Proverbs 20:30 (GNT)

• •

- God uses pain to bring good out of bad.

*"We know that in all things God works for the
good of those who love him."*
Romans 8:28 (NIV)

• •

- God uses pain to prepare you for eternity.

*"These little troubles are getting us ready for an eternal glory that will
make all our troubles seem like nothing. Things that are seen don't last
forever, but things that are not seen are eternal. That's why we keep our
minds on the things that cannot be seen."*
2 Corinthians 4:17-18 (CEV)

5. _____

*"We don't want you to be ignorant about those who have died. We don't
want you to grieve like other people who have no hope."*
1 Thessalonians 4:13 (GW)

*"[God] will wipe every tear from their eyes. There will be no
more death or mourning or crying or pain, for the old order
of things has passed away."*
Revelation 21:4 (NIV)

6. _____

"[God] comforts us in all our troubles, so that we can comfort those in any trouble with the comfort we ourselves receive from God."
2 Corinthians 1:4 (NIV)

Your greatest ministry will come out of your deepest hurt.

· ·

Every day, you either need comfort or you need
to comfort others.

DISCOVERY QUESTIONS

1. Pastor Rick told us, "If you don't let it out, you'll act it out." Share an example of a time you didn't grieve a loss. Did that grief show up later in an unhealthy way?

2. Share an experience where God has used your church family for support in your life.

3. Romans 8:28 says, "*We know that in all things God works for the good of those who love him*" (NIV). Think of a time in your life when God brought good out of bad. What good thing did God do? When did you first realize how God was working?

PUTTING IT INTO PRACTICE

Pastor Rick shared that every day we either need comfort or we need to comfort others. Which of these best describes you right now?

If you're in need of comfort, do you need to ask for help?

If you're in a place where you can comfort others, think of someone in your life who needs comfort right now. What are some practical ways you can make that happen?

PRAYER DIRECTION

As you pray together, ask God to help you heal from any losses that you still grieve. Expect God to answer your prayer.

Finally, pray that God will bring to mind anyone who is in need of comfort, and ask for opportunities that will allow you to step in and help. Look for ways he wants you to use your hurt to help others.

THE STRENGTH OF GENTLENESS

CHECKING IN

Last week Pastor Rick explained how God brings good out of bad. Did you see God at work this week, bringing good out of bad? If so, share that experience with the group.

KEY VERSE

*"God blesses those who are gentle.
The whole earth will belong to them!"*
Matthew 5:5

GENTLENESS IS _____

..

BENEFITS OF BEING GENTLE

1. GENTLENESS _____

"A gentle answer turns away wrath, but a harsh word stirs up anger."
Proverbs 15:1

When other people raise their voice, lower yours.

*"If your boss is angry at you, don't quit! A quiet spirit
can overcome even great mistakes."*
Ecclesiastes 10:4 (NLT)

2. GENTLENESS _____

"We respond gently when evil things are said about us."
1 Corinthians 4:13 (NLT)

*"Your conversation should be so sensible and logical that anyone who
wants to argue will be ashamed of himself because there won't be
anything to criticize in anything you say!"*
Titus 2:8 (TLB)

3. GENTLENESS _____

"Gentle speech breaks down rigid defenses."
Proverbs 25:15 (The Message)

"A gentle word can get through to the hard-headed."
Proverbs 25:15 (NCV)

*"A wise, mature person is known for understanding. The more pleasant
his words, the more persuasive he is."*
Proverbs 16:21 (GNT)

••

I'm never persuasive when I'm abrasive.

4. GENTLENESS _____

The Five Marks of a Godly Man or Woman:

"[As a] man of God . . . pursue what God approves of: a godly life, faith, love, endurance, and gentleness."
1 Timothy 6:11 (GW)

1) **Godliness: Being Christ-like**

2) **Faith: Trusting God in every area of life**

3) **Love: Being unselfish**

4) **Endurance: Refusing to quit**

5) **Gentleness: Strength under control**

"You should be known for the beauty that comes from within, the unfading beauty of a gentle and quiet spirit, which is so precious to God."
1 Peter 3:4 (NLT)

5. GENTLENESS _____

"Husbands, love your wives and be gentle with them."
Colossians 3:19 (NCV)

"Fathers, do not irritate and provoke your children to anger. Do not exasperate them to resentment, but rear them tenderly in the training and discipline and counsel of the Lord."
Ephesians 6:4 (AMP)

6. GENTLENESS

"Moses was very meek and a gentle man. In fact, he was more gentle than anyone else on the face of the earth!"
Numbers 12:3

7. GENTLENESS

"Believers should never speak evil of anyone, nor be quarrelsome. Instead, they should be gentle and show courtesy to everyone."
Titus 3:2

"Always be prepared to give an answer to everyone who asks you to give the reason for the hope that you have. But do this with gentleness and respect."
1 Peter 3:15 (NIV)

8. GENTLENESS

"Come to me, all you who are weary and burdened, and I will give you rest. Take my yoke upon you and learn from me, for I am gentle and humble in heart, and you will find rest for your souls."
Matthew 11:28-29 (NIV)

"The fruit of the Spirit is . . . gentleness."
Galatians 5:22-23 (NIV)

DISCOVERY QUESTIONS

1. In our culture, gentleness is usually thought of as a sign of weakness. Coming into small group today, what preconceptions did you have about gentleness? Did you view it as a positive or negative trait?

2. Being gentle with others has so many benefits and yet we often struggle with it in our daily lives. What's the hardest part for you about being gentle? For example, do you have to get in the last word during a disagreement? Do you struggle with anger issues? Do you tend to retaliate when you're hurt?

3. Think of a time when you set your pride aside and chose to be gentle with someone you didn't think deserved it. Did it change how that person responded to you? Did it change the way you viewed that person?

4. The Bible says in 1 Timothy 6:11, "[As a believer] . . . *pursue what God approves of: a godly life, faith, love, endurance, and gentleness.*" As you apply this verse in your life, what will that look like?

PUTTING IT INTO PRACTICE

Gentleness is not always the easiest or most natural reaction to conflict. How do you tend to react when faced with disagreements or disappointments?

What would it look like to respond with gentleness in those situations? Think of some tools to practice gentleness such as speaking softly and using pleasant words, and share them with the group.

PRAYER DIRECTION

As you pray together, ask God to give you opportunities this week to show gentleness. Ask him for the self-control you will need to lay aside your pride and respond to others with gentleness. Tell God you believe he will answer this prayer and that you will take a step of faith by practicing self-control.

YOUR MINISTRY OF MERCY

CHECKING IN

What opportunities has God given you to show gentleness to other people since the last meeting? How did they respond?

KEY VERSE

"God blesses those who are merciful, for they will be shown mercy."
Matthew 5:7

WHY BE MERCIFUL TO OTHERS?

1. _____

"God's mercy is so abundant, and his love for us is so great, that while we were spiritually dead in our disobedience he brought us to life with Christ. It is by God's grace that you have been saved."
Ephesians 2:4-5 (GNT)

2. _____

*"God has told you what is good and what he requires from you . . .
To do what is right with others, to love being merciful to others, and to
live humbly in fellowship with God."*
Micah 6:8

"I don't want your sacrifices! I want you to be merciful!"
Hosea 6:6

3. _____

*"You must show mercy to others, or God will not show mercy
to you . . . But the person who shows mercy can stand without
fear at the judgment."*
James 2:13 (NCV)

4. _____

*"If you want to be happy, be kind to those in need; it is
a sin to despise anyone."*
Proverbs 14:21 (GNT)

"A merciful person helps himself, but a cruel person hurts himself."
Proverbs 11:17 (GW)

"Your own soul is nourished when you show mercy."
Proverbs 11:17 (TLB)

HOW DO I BE MERCIFUL?

1. _____

"Be patient with each other, making allowance for each other's faults because of your love."
Ephesians 4:2 (TLB)

"The man who makes no allowances for others will find none made for him."
James 2:13 (PHILLIPS)

"The wisdom that comes from heaven is pure. It is also peace loving, gentle at all times, and willing to yield to others. Wisdom is full of mercy."
James 3:17 (NLT)

2. _____

"Whenever you possibly can, do good to those who need it."
Proverbs 3:27 (GNT)

"[When you do] acts of mercy, show mercy with cheerfulness."
Romans 12:8 (ASV)

"If you work with the disadvantaged, don't let yourself get irritated with them or depressed by them. Keep a smile on your face."
Romans 12:8 (The Message)

3. _____

"Don't get bitter or angry or use harsh words that hurt each other. Don't yell at one another or curse or ever be rude. Instead, be kind and merciful, and forgive others, just as God forgave you because of Christ."
Ephesians 4:31-32

4. _____

"Love your enemies, do good to them, and lend to them without expecting to get anything back. Then your reward will be great, and you will be children of the Most High, because he is kind to the ungrateful and wicked. Be merciful, just as your Father is merciful."

Luke 6:35-36 (NIV)

5. _____

"Even though I was once a blasphemer and a persecutor and a violent man, I was shown mercy because I acted in ignorance and unbelief . . . I was shown mercy so that in me, the worst of sinners, Christ Jesus might display his immense patience as an example for those who would believe in him and receive eternal life."

1 Timothy 1:13,16

"Show mercy to those who have doubts. Save others by snatching them from the fire. Show mercy to them, while being careful that you aren't contaminated by their sins."

Jude 1:22-23 (GW/NLT)

6. _____

"Matthew invited Jesus and his disciples to be his dinner guests, along with tax collectors and many other notorious sinners. The Pharisees were indignant. 'Why does your teacher eat with such scum?' they asked the disciples. When he heard this, Jesus replied, 'Healthy people don't need a doctor—sick people do. Go learn the meaning of the Scripture, "I want you to be merciful; I don't want your sacrifices! For I have come to call sinners, not those who think they are already good enough."'"

Matthew 9:10-13 (NLT)

7. _____

"Another time Jesus was walking through some grain fields on the Sabbath. His disciples were hungry, so they began to pick some grain and eat it. Some Pharisees saw this and protested, 'Your disciples are breaking God's law by harvesting grain on the Sabbath!' But Jesus said, 'Haven't you ever read what King David did when he and his soldiers were hungry? He went into the house of God, and they ate the holy bread reserved for the priests? . . . You would not have judged these innocent men if you knew the real meaning of the Scripture, "I want you to be merciful. I don't want your sacrifices! For I am the Lord of the Sabbath!"'"
Matthew 12:1-8 (NLT)

DISCOVERY QUESTIONS

1. Share with the group a time when you were in need (emotionally, physically, financially, etc.) and someone showed you mercy.

2. Pastor Rick taught that the people who have hurt us the most in life are in need of our mercy. Is there someone in the group who is willing to share how a deep hurt was overcome by showing mercy to someone else?

3. One way to show mercy is by building bridges of love to people who appear to be unlovable. How can we show mercy to people who offend us or rub us the wrong way?

PUTTING IT INTO PRACTICE

What is one way to show that you value relationships over rules?
How can you show that to someone this week?

Pastor Rick challenged us to commit an act of
premeditated mercy this week.

Pick one of the seven ways to practice mercy, and then
take a practical step toward loving someone who seems
unlovable or unpopular.

PRAYER DIRECTION

As you begin your prayer time, spend a moment in silent prayer,
asking God to reveal anyone in your life who needs your mercy.

Now pray for God to bring you opportunities to show mercy to
those people. Tell God you believe he will answer this prayer and
that you will be looking for those opportunities.

Finally, ask God for the patience you need to love people who
have quirks and weaknesses that irritate you.

HOW TO RECONCILE A RELATIONSHIP

CHECKING IN

In the last session, Pastor Rick challenged us to commit an act of premeditated mercy. How did you show mercy this week, and how did it affect you?

KEY VERSE

"God blesses those who are peacemakers, for they will be called the children of God."
Matthew 5:9 (NLT)

••

Misconceptions about peacemaking:

- Peacemaking is not avoiding.

- Peacemaking is not appeasing.

••

HOW TO BE A PEACEMAKER

1. _____

The only way to resolve a conflict is to face it.

"God has not given us a spirit of fear and timidity, but of power, love, and self-discipline."
2 Timothy 1:7 (NLT)

2. _____

"If you want to know what God wants you to do, ask him, and he will gladly tell you."
James 1:5 (TLB)

3. _____

The Causes of Conflict:

• Self-centeredness

"What causes fights and quarrels among you? They are caused by selfish desires that are continually at war inside you."
James 4:1

When I'm at peace inside, what's outside doesn't upset me.

• Pride

"Pride only leads to arguments."
Proverbs 13:10 (NCV)

4. _____

"Be quick to listen, slow to speak, and slow to get angry."
James 1:19 (NLT)

Always listen before speaking.

"Each of you should look not only to your own interests, but also to the interests of others. Your attitude should be the same as that of Christ Jesus."
Philippians 2:4-5 (NIV)

• •

"Seek to understand before seeking to be understood."
-Chinese Proverb

• •

"We must be considerate of the doubts and fears of others . . . Let's please the other fellow, not ourselves, and do what is for his good and thus build him up in the Lord."
Romans 15:2 (TLB)

5. _____

"Speak the truth in love."
Ephesians 4:15 (NLT)

"Reckless words pierce like a sword, but the tongue of the wise brings healing."
Proverbs 12:18 (NIV)

"Do not use harmful words, but only helpful words, the kind that build up and provide what is needed."
Ephesians 4:29 (GNT)

6. _____

"You must also rid yourselves of all such things as these: anger, rage, malice, slander, and filthy language from your lips."
Colossians 3:8 (NIV)

7. _____

- **Reconciliation:** Reestablishing the relationship

- **Resolution:** Resolving every disagreement

"[God] has restored our relationship with him through Christ, and has given us this ministry of restoring relationships . . . . God was in Christ restoring his relationship with humanity. He didn't hold people's faults against them, and he has given us this message of restored relationships to tell others. We are Christ'srepresentatives . . . . We beg you on behalf of Christ to become reunited with God."
2 Corinthians 5:18-20 (GW)

DISCOVERY QUESTIONS

1. Give an example of someone you consider to be a peacemaker. What qualities does that person exhibit that help him or her handle conflict well?

2. In a typical conflict, there are skunks and there are turtles. Skunks stink the place up and let everyone know they're unhappy. Turtles pull into their shell and hide. Which one best describes you?

3. Look back at the seven steps to resolving conflict and restoring a broken relationship. Which step is the hardest for you?

4. Pastor Rick stated that we're most like Jesus when we're focusing on the hurts of others rather than on ourselves. What obstacles may be distracting you from focusing on someone else's hurts? Are you struggling with pride? Do you tend to speak first and listen later?

5. What would it sound like to speak the truth in love?

PUTTING IT INTO PRACTICE

Who do you need to have a peace conference with this week? What broken relationship needs mending? What conflict have you been avoiding?

What are some practical steps you can take to make the first move and break down the walls of conflict?

PRAYER DIRECTION

Ask God to bring to your mind any relationships that are in need of restoration. Then ask God for the wisdom to know how and when to approach that person.

Finally, ask God to give you his courage to follow through, and tell God you will faithfully take the first step in reconciling the relationship.

HANDLING OPPOSITION TO YOUR FAITH

CHECKING IN

How did your peace conference go this week? When you took the first step, was it easier or harder than you expected? If you feel comfortable, share your experience with the group.

KEY VERSE

"God blesses those who are persecuted for doing right, for the Kingdom of Heaven is theirs."
Matthew 5:10-12 (NLT)

• •

"Remember those who are in prison, as if you were in prison with them. Remember those who are suffering, as if you were suffering with them."
Hebrews 13:3

"Anyone who belongs to Christ Jesus and wants to live right will have trouble from others."
2 Timothy 3:12 (CEV)

WHAT TO REMEMBER

1. _____

"When the world hates you, remember it hated me first. The world would love you if you belonged to it, but you don't. I chose you out of the world. That's why the world will hate you. No servant is ever greater than his master. So since they persecuted me, they will persecute you too."
John 15:18-20

"The light from heaven came into the world, but people love their darkness more than the light, because it hides their evil actions."
John 3:19

"If you're abused because of Christ, count yourself fortunate. It's the Spirit of God and his glory in you that brought you to the notice of others."
1 Peter 4:14 (The Message)

2. _____

"These troubles will prove that you faith is genuine. Just as gold is purified by fire and heat, so your faith, which is far more precious than gold, must also be purified by fire so it may endure. Then you'll receive praise and glory and honor on the Day when Jesus Christ is revealed to the whole world."
1 Peter 1:7

3. _____

"God blesses those who are persecuted because they live for God: the Kingdom of Heaven will be theirs! You will be blessed when people insult you, and persecute you and falsely say all kinds of evil against

you because of me. Rejoice and be glad, because great is your reward in
heaven, for in the same way they persecuted the
prophets who were before you."
Matthew 5:10-12

WHAT TO DO

1. _____

"Dear friends, don't be surprised or shocked when you go through
painful trials that are like walking through fire, as though something
unusual is happening to you."
1 Peter 4:12 (CEV/GNT)

2. _____

"If you suffer for doing what is right, God will reward you for it, so don't
be afraid and don't worry! Instead, worship Christ as Lord of your life.
And if you are asked about your Christian hope,
always be ready to explain it."
1 Peter 3:14-15 (NLT)

3. _____

"It is no shame to suffer for being a Christian. Instead, thank God
for the privilege of being called by his name!"
1 Peter 4:16 (NLT)

I don't need other people's approval to be happy.

"Take a firm stand against Satan, and be strong in your faith. Remember that your Christian brothers and sisters all over the world are going through the same kind of suffering you are."

1 Peter 5:9 (NLT)

"Remember, it is better to suffer for doing God's will than to suffer for doing evil."

1 Peter 3:17

4. _____

"Stay away from stupid and senseless arguments. These only lead to trouble. God's servants must never quarrel. Be kind to everyone . . . and be patient. Be humble when you correct people who oppose you . . . . they've been trapped by the devil, and he makes them obey him, but God may help them escape."

2 Timothy 2:23-26 (CEV)

5. _____

"Never pay back evil with more evil . . . If it is possible, as far as it depends on you, live at peace with everyone. And never avenge yourself. Leave that to God, who has said, 'I'll be the judge and I'll take care of it.'"

Romans 12:17-19

6. _____

"Do not be overcome by evil, but overcome evil with good."

Romans 12:21 (ESV)

"Love your enemies! Do good to those who hate you. Bless those who curse you. Pray for those who hurt you. If someone slaps you on one cheek, turn the other cheek."

Luke 6:27-29 (NLT)

DISCOVERY QUESTIONS

1. The Bible promises that, as believers, we will face opposition at some point in our lives. Share a time when you faced opposition because of your faith and what the experience taught you.

2. Second Timothy 2:23-26 tells us to stay away from senseless arguments with other believers. It also says we should be kind and humble to anyone who opposes us. How can we avoid the trap of getting into arguments with other believers, particularly on social media? What are some ways that we can be patient and humble when we're speaking to others who don't share our beliefs?

PUTTING IT INTO PRACTICE

Imagine it is illegal to be a Christian where you live, and everyone who follows Jesus is arrested and put in prison. Would there be enough evidence to convict you of being a Christ follower? What is your faith costing you?

Ask God to tell you a courageous step of faith he wants you to take this week. God will start by giving you small steps, because he wants to build your faith. He may ask you to do something small or simple, but the important thing is to do what he says.

Then God may ask you to take a bigger step of faith, such as being baptized. Whatever step God asks of you, you can trust that he knows you're ready.

PRAYER DIRECTION

As we wrap up this series, begin the prayer time by thanking God for all he has taught you through this Bible study. Thank him for helping you grow and for challenging you to put your beliefs into action.

Ask God to help you faithfully use the courage that he gives you to speak up for your faith and to do the Christ-like thing, even when it's unpopular.

SMALL GROUP RESOURCES

Small Group Resources

HELP FOR HOSTS

TOP 10 IDEAS FOR NEW HOSTS

CONGRATULATIONS! As the host of your small group, you have responded to the call to help shepherd Jesus' flock. Few other tasks in the family of God surpass the contribution you will be making. As you prepare to facilitate your group, whether it is one session or the entire series, here are a few thoughts to keep in mind.

Remember you are not alone. God knows everything about you, and he knew you would be asked to facilitate your group. Even though you may not feel ready, this is common for all good hosts. God promises, *"I will never leave you; I will never abandon you"* (Hebrews 13:5 GNT). Whether you are facilitating for one evening, several weeks, or a lifetime, you will be blessed as you serve.

1. **DON'T TRY TO DO IT ALONE.** Pray right now for God to help you build a healthy team. If you can enlist a co-host to help you shepherd the group, you will find your experience much richer. This is your chance to involve as many people as you can in building a healthy group. All you have to do is ask people to help. You'll be surprised at the response.

2. **BE FRIENDLY AND BE YOURSELF.** God wants to use your unique gifts and temperament. Be sure to greet people at the door with a big smile . . . this can set

the mood for the whole gathering. Remember, they are taking as big a step to show up at your house as you are to host a small group! Don't try to do things exactly like another host; do them in a way that fits you. Admit when you don't have an answer and apologize when you make a mistake. Your group will love you for it and you'll sleep better at night.

3. **PREPARE FOR YOUR MEETING AHEAD OF TIME**. Review the session and write down your responses to each question. Pay special attention to the **Putting It Into Practice** exercises that ask group members to do something other than engage in discussion. These exercises will help your group live what the Bible teaches, not just talk about it.

4. **PRAY FOR YOUR GROUP MEMBERS BY NAME.** Before you begin your session, take a few moments and pray for each member by name. You may want to review the **Small Group Prayer and Praise Report** at least once a week. Ask God to use your time together to touch the heart of each person in your group. Expect God to lead you to whomever he wants you to encourage or challenge in a special way. If you listen, God will surely lead.

5. **WHEN YOU ASK A QUESTION, BE PATIENT.** Someone will eventually respond. Sometimes people need a moment or two of silence to think about the question. If silence doesn't bother you, it won't bother anyone else. After someone responds, affirm the response with a simple "thanks" or "great answer." Then ask, "How about somebody else?" or "Would someone who hasn't shared like to add anything?" Be sensitive to new people or reluctant members who aren't ready to say, pray, or do anything. If you give them a safe setting, they will blossom over time. If someone in your group is a wallflower who sits silently through every session, consider talking to them privately and encouraging them to participate. Let them know how important they are to

you—that they are loved and appreciated, and that the group would value their input. Remember, still water often runs deep.

6. **PROVIDE TRANSITIONS BETWEEN QUESTIONS.** Ask if anyone would like to read the paragraph or Bible passage. Don't call on anyone, but ask for a volunteer, and then be patient until someone begins. Be sure to thank the person who reads aloud.

7. **BREAK INTO SMALLER GROUPS OCCASIONALLY.** With a greater opportunity to talk in a small circle, people will connect more with the study, apply more quickly what they're learning, and ultimately get more out of their small group experience. A small circle also encourages a quiet person to participate and tends to minimize the effects of a more vocal or dominant member.

8. **SMALL CIRCLES ARE ALSO HELPFUL DURING PRAYER TIME.** People who are unaccustomed to praying aloud will feel more comfortable trying it with just two or three others. Also, prayer requests won't take as much time, so circles will have more time to actually pray. When you gather back with the whole group, you can have one person from each circle briefly update everyone on the prayer requests from their subgroups. The other great aspect of subgrouping is that it fosters leadership development. As you ask people in the group to facilitate discussion or to lead a prayer circle, it gives them a small leadership step that can build their confidence.

9. **ROTATE FACILITATORS OCCASIONALLY.** You may be perfectly capable of hosting each time, but you will help others grow in their faith and gifts if you give them opportunities to host the group.

10. **ONE FINAL CHALLENGE (FOR NEW OR FIRST-TIME HOSTS).** Before your first opportunity to lead, look up each of the six passages listed below. Read each one

as a devotional exercise to help prepare you with a shepherd's heart.

When [Jesus] saw the crowds, he had compassion on them, because they were harassed and helpless, like sheep without a shepherd. Then he said to his disciples, "The harvest is plentiful but the workers are few. Ask the Lord of the harvest, therefore, to send out workers into his harvest field."
Matthew 9:36–38 (NIV)

I am the good shepherd; I know my sheep and my sheep know me—just as the Father knows me and I know the Father—and I lay down my life for the sheep.
John 10:14–15 (NIV)

Be shepherds of God's flock that is under your care, serving as overseers—not because you must, but because you are willing, as God wants you to be; not greedy for money, but eager to serve; not lording it over those entrusted to you, but being examples to the flock. And when the Chief Shepherd appears, you will receive the crown of glory that will never fade away.
1 Peter 5:2–4 (NIV)

If you have any encouragement from being united with Christ, if any comfort from his love, if any fellowship with the Spirit, if any tenderness and compassion, then make my joy complete by being like-minded, having the same love, being one in spirit and purpose. Do nothing out of selfish ambition or vain conceit, but in humility consider others better than yourselves. Each of you should look not only to your own interests, but also to the interests of others. Your attitude should be the same as that of Christ Jesus.
Philippians 2:1–5 (NIV)

Let us hold unswervingly to the hope we profess, for he who promised is faithful. And let us consider how we may spur one another on toward love and good deeds. Let us not give up meeting together, as some are in the habit of doing, but let us encourage one another— and all the more as you see the Day approaching.

Hebrews 10:23–25 (NIV)

But we were gentle among you, like a mother caring for her little children. We loved you so much that we were delighted to share with you not only the Gospel of God but our lives as well, because you had become so dear to us. For you know that we dealt with each of you as a father deals with his own children, encouraging, comforting and urging you to live lives worthy of God, who calls you into his kingdom and glory.

1 Thessalonians 2:7–8, 11–12 (NIV)

FREQUENTLY ASKED QUESTIONS

How long will this group meet?

This study is six sessions long. We encourage your group to add a seventh session for a celebration. In your final session, each group member may decide if he or she desires to continue on for another study. At that time you may also want to do some informal evaluation, discuss your group guidelines, and decide which study you want to do next. We recommend you visit our website at **PastorRick.com** for more video-based small group studies.

Who is the host?

The host is the person who coordinates and facilitates your group meetings. In addition to a host, we encourage you to select one or more group members to lead your group discussions. Several other responsibilities can be rotated, including serving refreshments, overseeing prayer requests, facilitating worship, or keeping up with those who miss a meeting. Shared ownership in the group helps everybody grow.

Where do we find new group members?

Recruiting new members can be a challenge for groups, especially new groups with just a few people, or existing groups that lose a few people along the way. We encourage you to use the **Circles of Life** diagram on page 56 of this study guide to brainstorm a list of people from your workplace, church, school, neighborhood, family, and so on. Then pray for the people on each member's list. Allow each member to invite several people from their list. Some groups fear that newcomers will interrupt the intimacy that members have built over time. However, groups that welcome newcomers generally gain strength with the infusion of new blood. Remember, the next person you add just might become a friend for eternity. Logistically, groups find different ways to add members. Some groups remain permanently open, while others choose to open periodically, such as at the beginning or end of a study. If your group becomes too large for easy, face-to-face conversations, you can subgroup, forming a second discussion group in another room.

How do we handle the childcare needs in our group?

Childcare needs must be handled very carefully. This is a sensitive issue. We suggest you seek creative solutions as a group. One common solution is to have the adults meet in the living room and share the cost of a baby sitter (or two) who can be with the kids in another part of the house.

Another popular option is to have one home for the kids and a second home (close by) for the adults. If desired, the adults could rotate the responsibility of providing a lesson for the kids. This last option is great with school-age kids and can be a huge blessing to families.

CIRCLES OF LIFE

SMALL GROUP CONNECTIONS

Discover Who You Can Connect in Community
Use this chart to help carry out one of the values in the Group Guidelines, to "Welcome Newcomers."

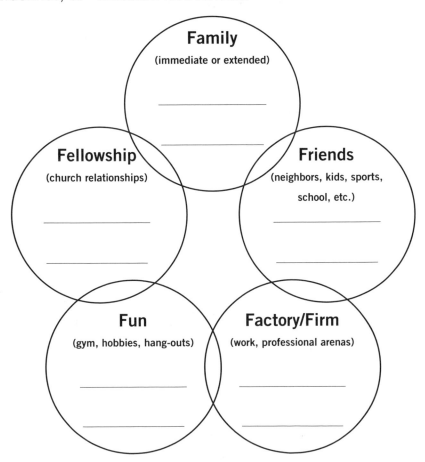

Family
(immediate or extended)

_____

_____

Fellowship
(church relationships)

_____

_____

Friends
(neighbors, kids, sports, school, etc.)

_____

_____

Fun
(gym, hobbies, hang-outs)

_____

_____

Factory/Firm
(work, professional arenas)

_____

_____

Follow this simple three-step process:

1. List one to two people in each circle.

2. Prayerfully select one person or couple from your list and tell your group about them.

3. Give them a call and invite them to your next meeting. Over fifty percent of those invited to a small group say, "Yes!"

GROUP GUIDELINES

It's a good idea for every group to put words to their shared values, expectations, and commitments. Such guidelines will help you avoid unspoken agendas and unmet expectations. We recommend you discuss your guidelines during Session 1 in order to lay the foundation for a healthy group experience. Feel free to modify anything that does not work for your group.

We agree to the following values:

CLEAR PURPOSE	To grow healthy spiritual lives by building a healthy small group community
GROUP ATTENDANCE	To give priority to the group meeting (call if I am absent or late)
SAFE ENVIRONMENT	To create a safe place where people can be heard and feel loved (no quick answers, snap judgments, or simple fixes)
BE CONFIDENTIAL	To keep anything that is shared strictly confidential and within the group
CONFLICT RESOLUTION	To avoid gossip and to immediately resolve any concerns by following the principles of Matthew 18:15–17

SPIRITUAL HEALTH   To give group members permission to speak into my life and help me live a healthy, balanced spiritual life that is pleasing to God

LIMIT OUR FREEDOM   To limit our freedom by not serving or consuming alcohol during small group meetings or events so as to avoid causing a weaker brother or sister to stumble (1 Corinthians 8:1–13; Romans 14:19–21)

WELCOME NEWCOMERS   To invite friends who might benefit from this study and warmly welcome newcomers

BUILDING RELATIONSHIPS   To get to know the other members of the group and pray for them regularly

OTHER   _____
_____
_____

We have also discussed and agree on the following items:

CHILD CARE   _____

STARTING TIME   _____

ENDING TIME   _____

If you haven't already done so, take a few minutes to fill out the **Small Group Calendar** on page 62.

SMALL GROUP PRAYER AND PRAISE REPORT

This is a place where you can write each other's requests for prayer. You can also make a note when God answers a prayer. Pray for each other's requests. If you're new to group prayer, it's okay to pray silently or to pray by using just one sentence:

"God, please help _____ to _____ ."

DATE	PERSON	PRAYER REQUEST	PRAISE REPORT

DATE	PERSON	PRAYER REQUEST	PRAISE REPORT

SMALL GROUP CALENDAR

Healthy groups share responsibilities and group ownership. It might take some time for this to develop. Shared ownership ensures that responsibility for the group doesn't fall to one person. Use the calendar to keep track of social events, mission projects, birthdays, or days off. Complete this calendar at your first or second meeting. Planning ahead will increase attendance and shared ownership.

DATE	LESSON	LOCATION	FACILITATOR	SNACK OR MEAL
	Session 1			
	Session 2			
	Session 3			

DATE	LESSON	LOCATION	FACILITATOR	SNACK OR MEAL
	Session 4			
	Session 5			
	Session 6			
	Celebration			

ANSWER KEY

SESSION 1:
IT DEPENDS ON WHO YOU DEPEND ON

To be "poor in spirit" means **I humbly depend on God instead of myself**.

5 Ways to Express My Dependence on God

1. **I depend on God's wisdom, not mine.**
2. **I depend on God's strength, not mine.**
3. **I depend on God's timing, not mine.**
4. **I depend on God's defense, not mine.**
5. **I depend on God's wealth, not mine.**

SESSION 2:
HOW GOD BLESSES BROKEN HEARTS

God doesn't expect me to be **happy all the time**.

Grief is essential to your health.

How Does God Bless Broken Hearts?

1. **He draws us in close to himself.**
2. **God grieves with us.**
3. **God gives us a church family for support.**
4. **God uses grief to help us grow.**
5. **God gives us the hope of heaven.**
6. **God uses our pain to help others.**

SESSION 3:
THE STRENGTH OF GENTLENESS

Gentleness is **strength under control**.

Benefits of Being Gentle

1. Gentleness **defuses conflict**.
2. Gentleness **disarms critics**.
3. Gentleness **is persuasive**.
4. Gentleness **is attractive**.
5. Gentleness **communicates love**.
6. Gentleness **earns respect**.
7. Gentleness **is a witness to unbelievers**.
8. Gentleness **makes me like Jesus**.

SESSION 4:
YOUR MINISTRY OF MERCY

Why Be Merciful to Others?

1. **God has shown me mercy.**
2. **God commands me to be merciful.**
3. **I'm going to need more mercy in the future.**
4. **Showing mercy brings or causes happiness.**

How Do I Be Merciful?

1. **Be patient with people's quirks.**
2. **Help anyone hurting around me.**
3. **Give people a second chance.**
4. **Do good to those who hurt me.**
5. **Be kind to those who offend me.**
6. **Build bridges of love to the unpopular.**
7. **Value relationships over rules.**

SESSION 5:

HOW TO RECONCILE A RELATIONSHIP

How to Be a Peacemaker

1. Make the first move.
2. Ask God for wisdom.
3. I begin with what's my fault.
4. Listen for their hurt and perspective.
5. Speak the truth tactfully!
6. Fix the problem, not the blame!
7. Focus on reconciliation, not resolution.

SESSION 6:

HANDLING OPPOSITION TO YOUR FAITH

What to Remember

1. Opposition can make me more like Jesus.
2. Opposition will deepen my faith.
3. Opposition will give me eternal rewards.

What to Do

1. Don't be surprised.
2. Don't be afraid.
3. Don't be ashamed.
4. Recognize the source of the opposition.
5. Refuse to retaliate.
6. Respond with a blessing.

KEY VERSES

SESSION 1

"Blessed are the poor in spirit, for theirs is the kingdom of heaven."
Matthew 5:3 (NIV)

SESSION 2

"God blesses those who mourn, for they will be comforted."
Matthew 5:4 (NLT)

SESSION 3

*"God blesses those who are gentle.
The whole earth will belong to them!"*
Matthew 5:5

SESSION 4

"God blesses those who are merciful, for they will be shown mercy."
Matthew 5:7

SESSION 5

*"God blesses those who are peacemakers, for they will
be called the children of God."*
Matthew 5:9 (NLT)

SESSION 6

*"God blesses those who are persecuted for doing right, for
the Kingdom of Heaven is theirs."*
Matthew 5:10-12 (NLT)

ADDITIONAL NOTES

ADDITIONAL NOTES

ADDITIONAL NOTES

MORE SPIRITUAL GROWTH TOOLS FROM PASTOR RICK

LIVING IN THE GOODNESS OF GOD

Dig deep into Psalm 23, experiencing God's unrelenting love for you, and discover why this passage can become the foundation for your faith.

DAILY HOPE PRAYER JOURNAL

Learn how to pray prayers that expect answers! Your faith will be strengthened and you will be blessed as you look back on your written prayers and see how God has faithfully answered them.

THE HABITS OF HAPPINESS

Discover the biblical habits of happiness and begin seeing things from God's perspective. You'll learn how happiness runs deeper than any circumstance, feeling, or relationship because of God's love for you.

OPEN DOORS: A YEAR OF DAILY DEVOTIONS

Be encouraged, inspired, and equipped to live out God's plan and purpose for your life when you open the door to a deeper relationship with him.